NEIL A. KJOS
PIANO LIBRARY

LEVEL NINE

PIANO REPERTOIRE

SELECTED & EDITED BY

Keith Snell

Etudes

CONTENTS

ISBN 0-8497-6243-X

Arpeggio Etude

Op. 105, No. 1

Friedrich Burgmüller
(1806-1874)

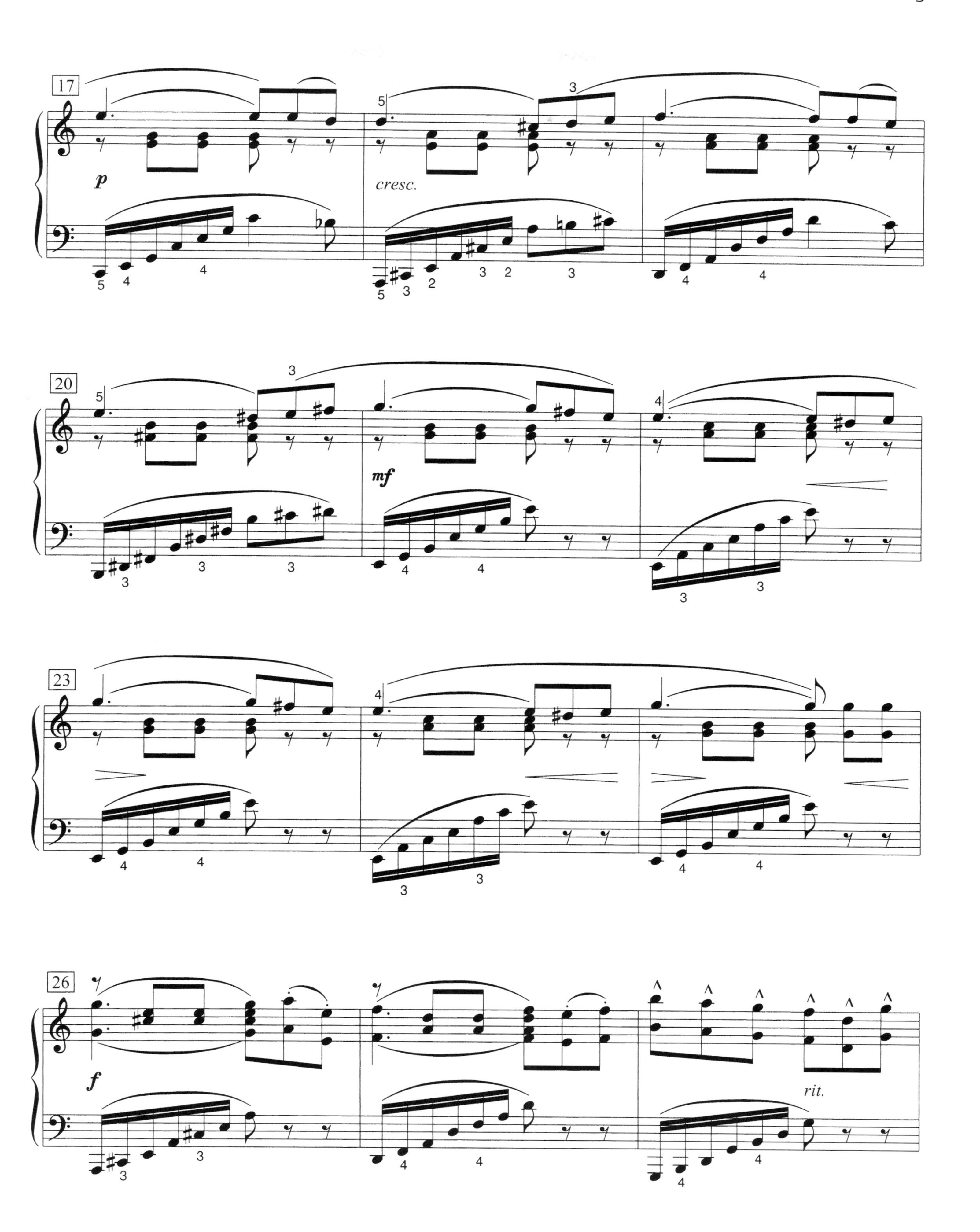
17
p
cresc.
20
mf
23
26
f
rit.

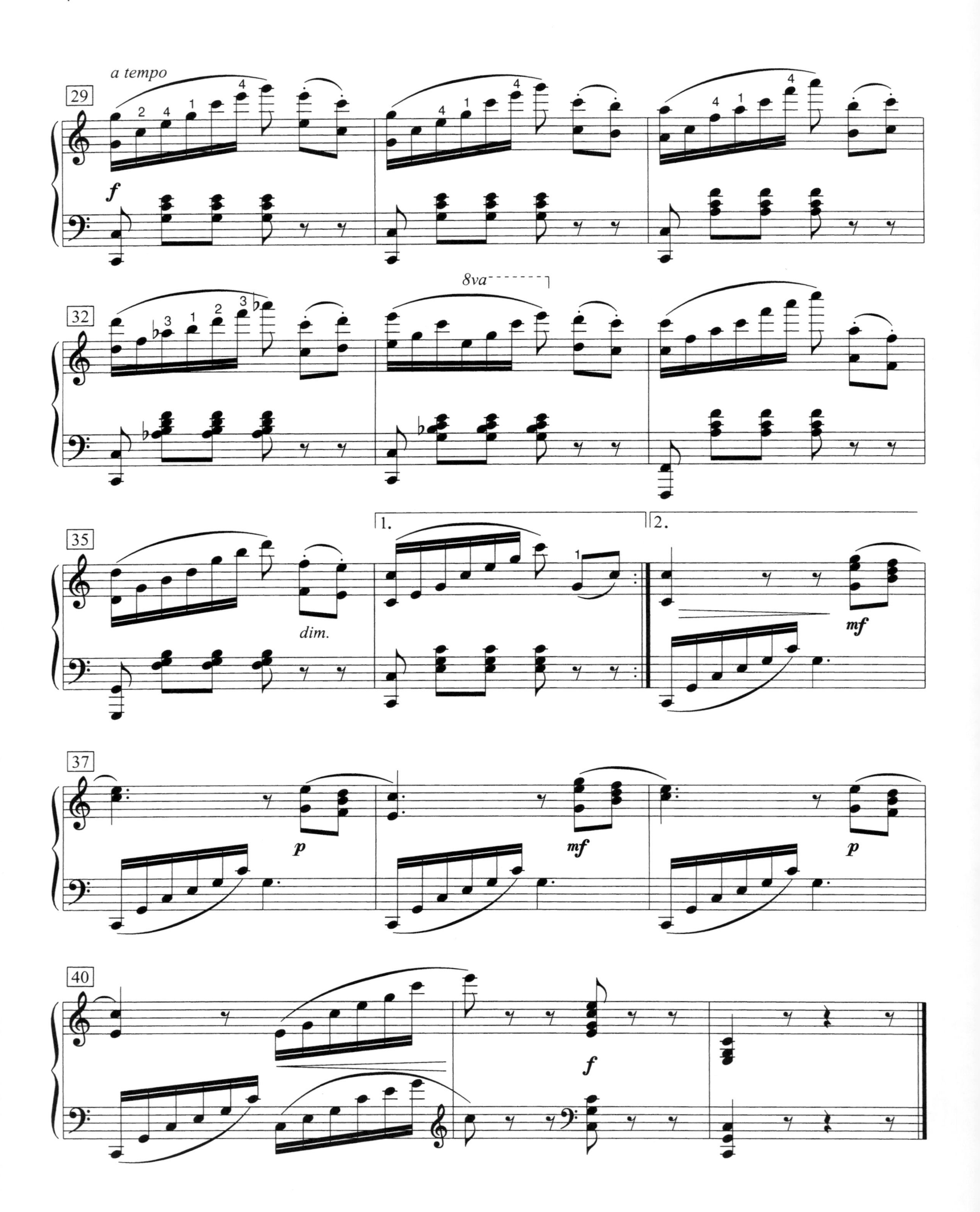
a tempo
29
8va
32
35
1.
2.
dim.
37
40

Octave Etude

Op. 105, No. 9

Friedrich Burgmüller
(1806-1874)

17
a tempo
p
cresc.
21
p
dim.
25
p
cresc.
29
f
dim. e rit.
p
33
f
cresc.
f

37
sf
f
dim. e rit.
41
a tempo
p
45
f
49
sf
sf
cresc.
8va
sf
sf
53
ff

Novelette

Op. 45, No. 17

Stephen Heller
(1814-1888)

17
p
20
f
p
23
8va
26
8va
f
sf
sf
sf
cresc.
30
8va
ff
sff
Fine

57
p
f
61
65
fp
pp
70
mf
f
74
ff
ff
8va
sff
D. C. al Fine

Prelude

Op. 81, No. 3

Stephen Heller
(1814-1888)

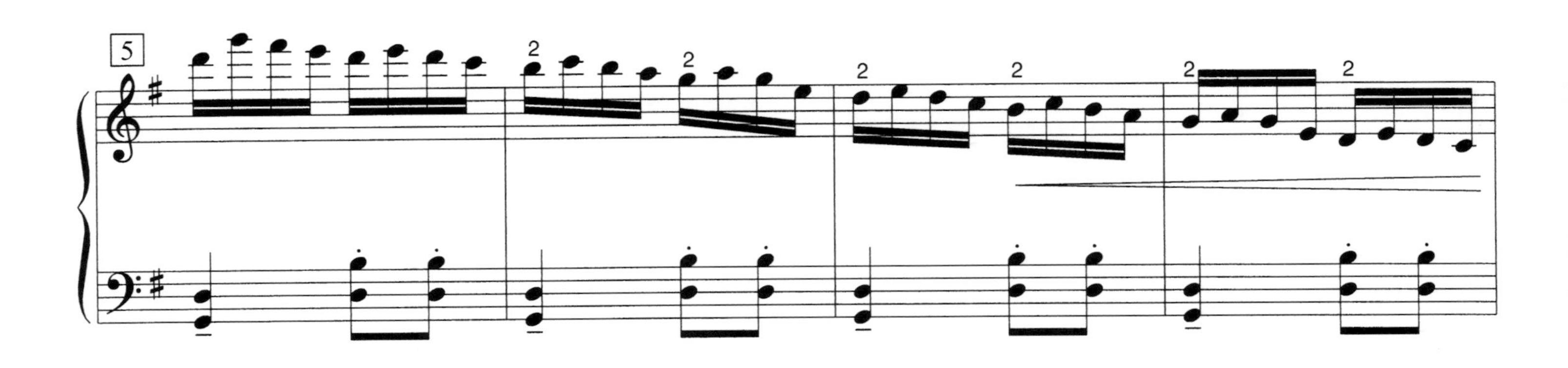

17
f
21
ff
25
f
ff
29
sff
p
f
p
pedal
34
f
p
rit.

a tempo
p
f
f
ff
sff
p
f
p
f
pedal
p
sff
rit.
a tempo
p

62
66
rit.
a tempo
70
cresc.
74
78

Etude

Op. 1, No. 4

Franz Liszt
(1811-1886)

21
8va
2
1
f
3
5
2
1
25
4
3
sf
p
29
33
37

41
p
45
49
cresc.
53
f

57
8va
ff
5
1
2
5
61
3
2
8va
5
3
2
65
r.h.
p
cresc.
69
8va
f
8va
73
8va
8va
ff
3

Scherzino

Op. 39, No. 11

Edward MacDowell
(1860-1908)

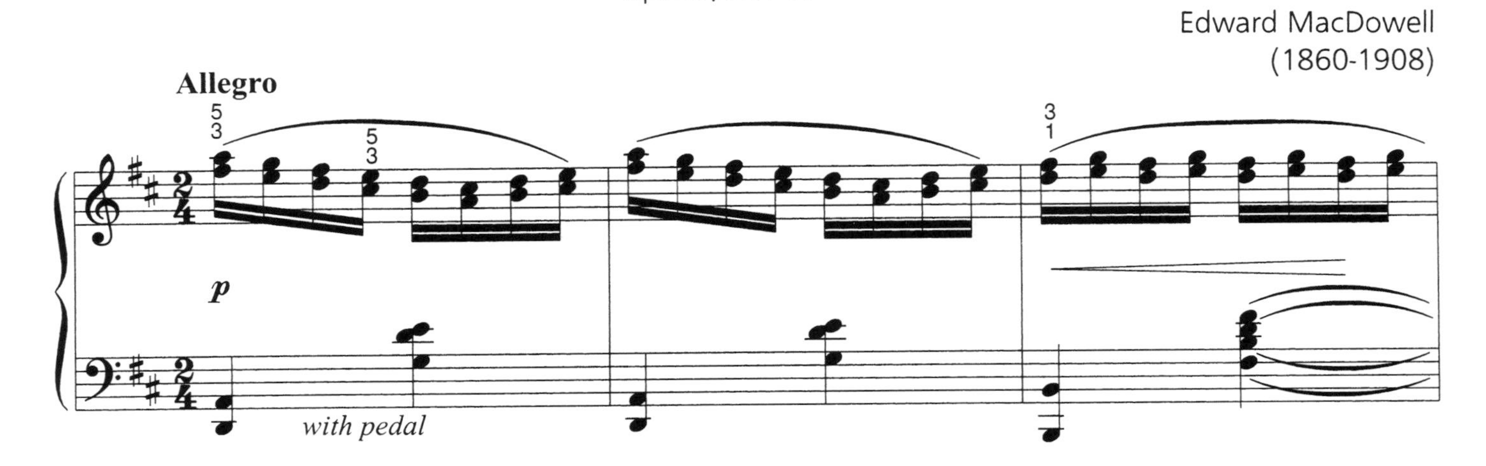

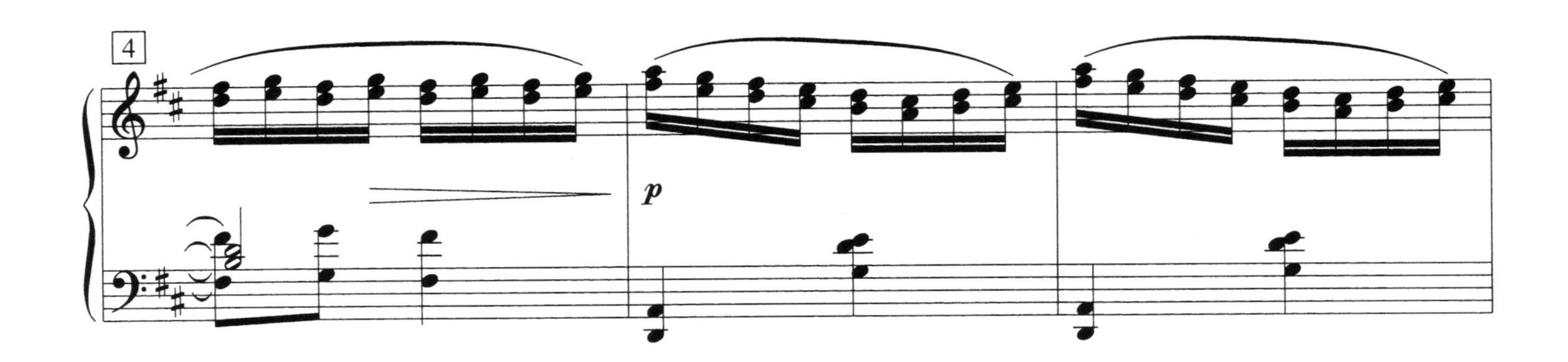

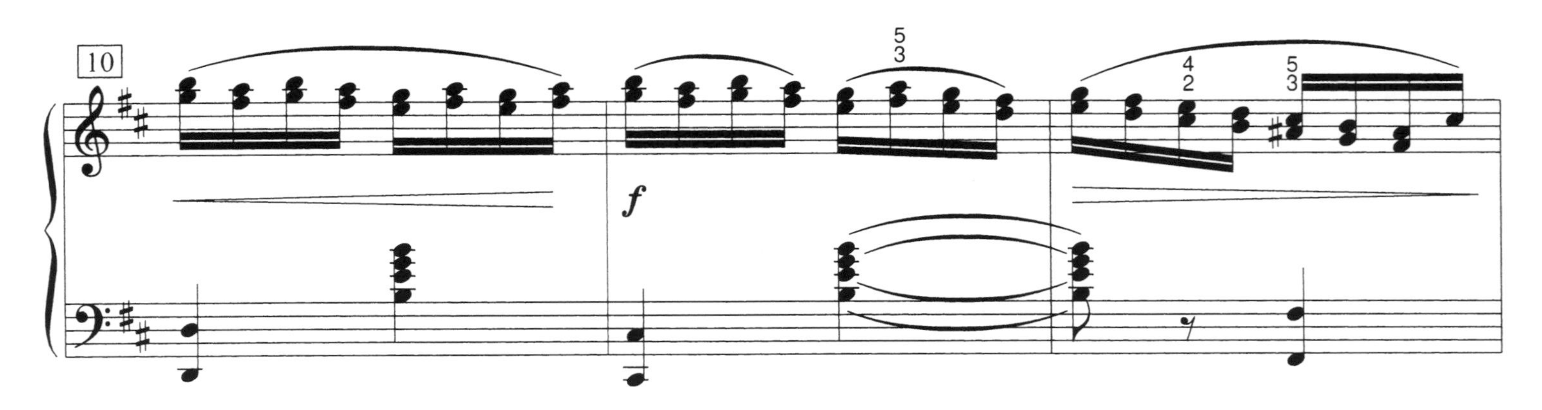

13
pp
16
f
19
p
22
pp
ppp

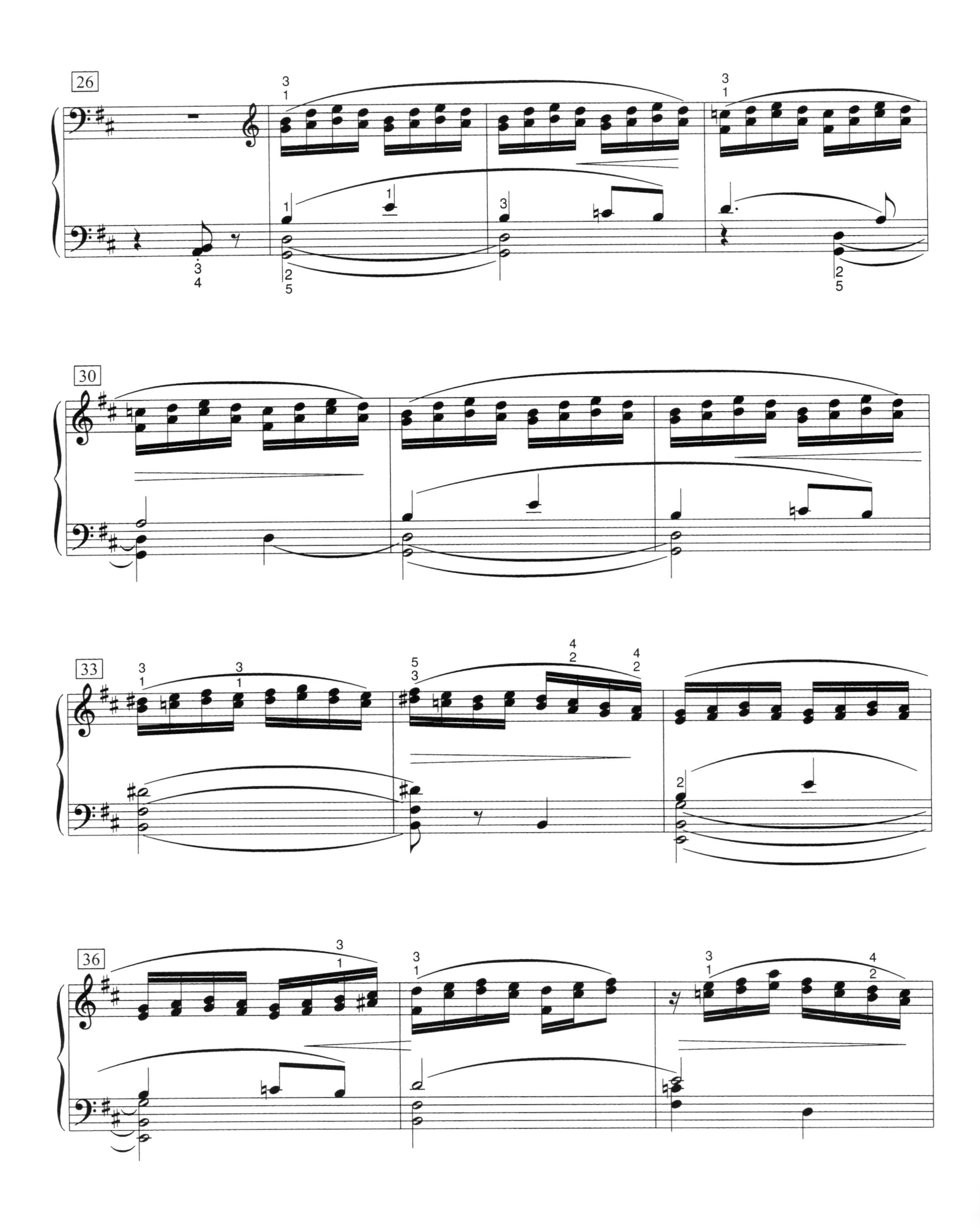

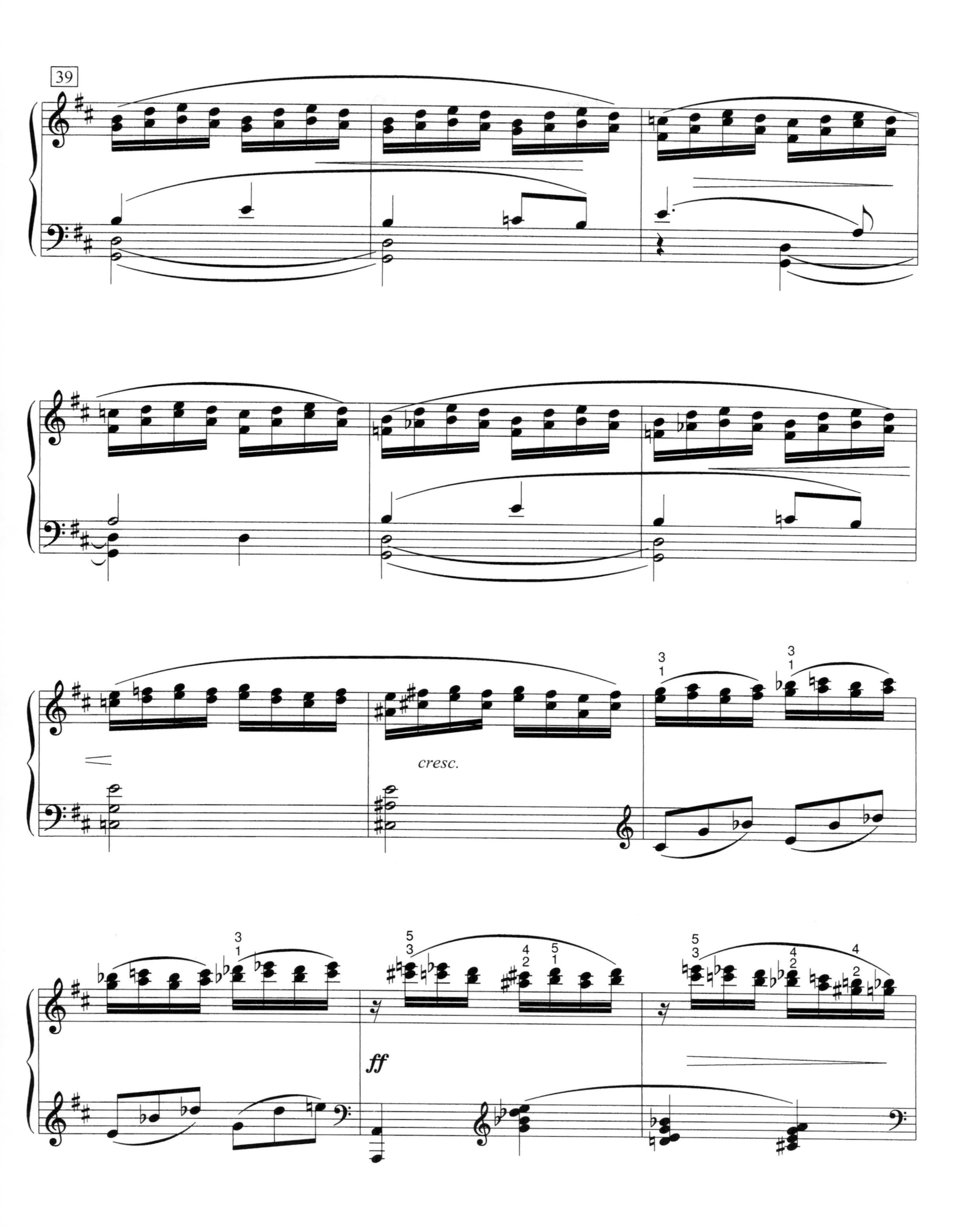
39
cresc.
ff

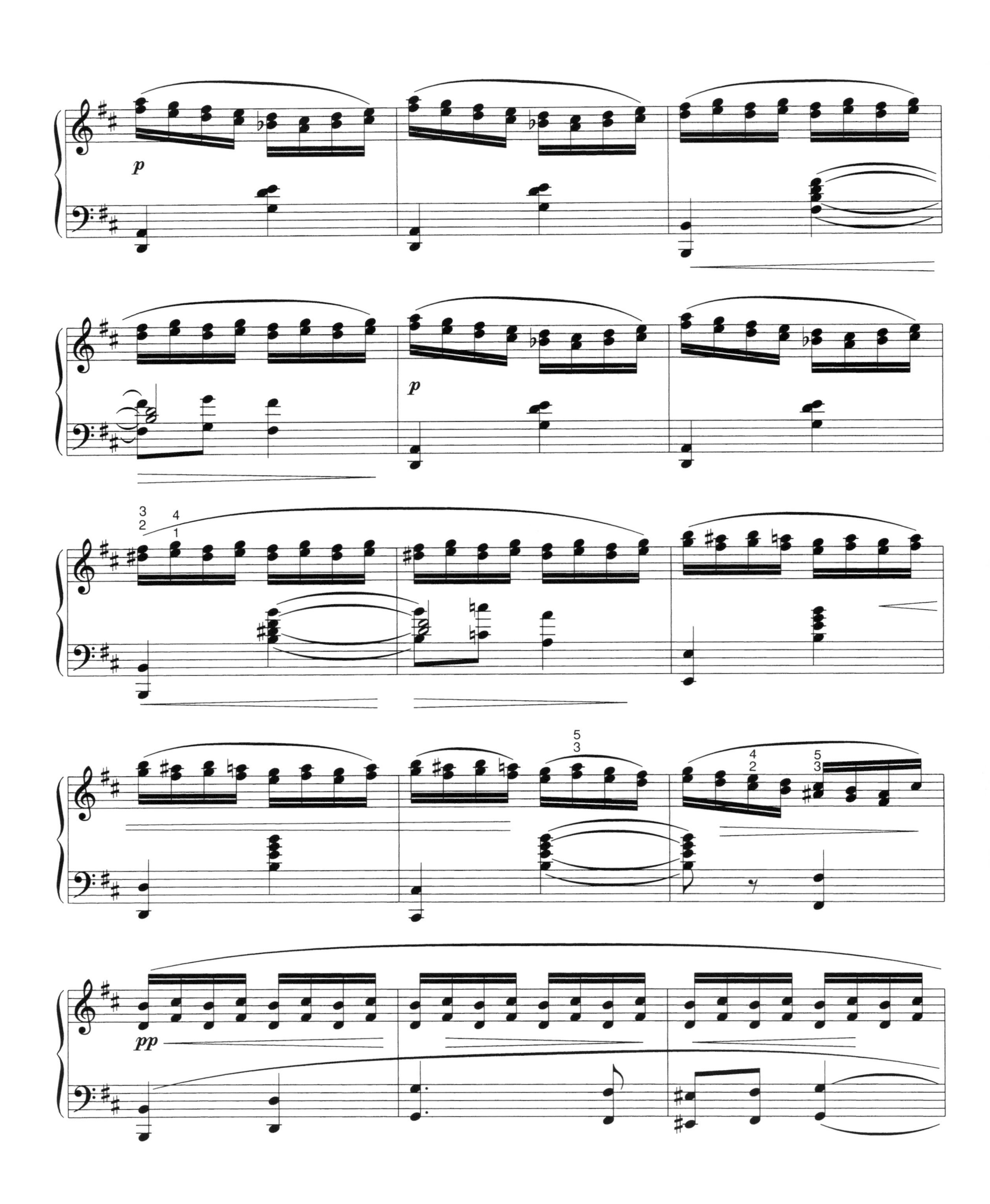

p
p
3
2
4
1
5
3
4
2
5
3
pp

p
pp
ppp
Vivo
leggieriss.
8va
ppp

Hungarian

Op. 39, No. 12

Edward MacDowell
(1860-1908)

21
8va
mf
25
8va
29
p
dim.
pp
33
ff
mf
cresc.
37
ff

mf
ff
p
cresc.
f
dim.
p

61
p
65
cresc.
8va
fz
69
f
73
ff
fz
77
8va
f
poco dim.

81
3
ff
85
4
pp
89
4
p
93
cresc.
simile
97
molto cresc.
8va
fz

101
8va
ff
f
105
8va
ff
f
109
8va
sfz
113
dim.
pp
117
8va
ff
sffz

ABOUT THE EDITOR

Keith Snell teaches preschool through advanced students in his private studio in California. He has trained students who have been accepted at the nation's leading conservatories and prepared avocational students for a lifetime of music enjoyment. His students participate regularly in recitals, auditions, festivals and contests. Keith received his B.M. and M.M. in Piano Performance from the University of Southern California where he was a piano student of John Perry and a pedagogy student of Marienne Uszler. He made his London debut in 1984 as winner of the Joanna Hodges International Piano Competition. Keith subsequently signed with Columbia Artist Management and recorded for Virgin Records thereby establishing a first-class performing career appearing as recitalist, in chamber music, and as soloist with distinguished orchestras. Keith brings his experience as both a pianist and teacher to his work for the Neil A. Kjos Music Company. He is editor of the highly acclaimed Neil A. Kjos *Master Composer Library,* and producer for Academy Records *Piano Literature Recordings*.